Contents

Introduction

It is estimated that about five out of every six animal species in the world are insects, occupying every niche in almost every habitat on the planet (the Polar regions and the deep oceans being the exceptions). Of the million or so named insect species across the globe, around 20,000 are found in Britain.

The varied landscapes of Cornwall and the Isles of Scilly offer many diverse wildlife habitats. From coastal fringes to moorland peaks, rivers and streams to woodlands and heaths, farmland to the mining landscape of the past, even our own domestic gardens – each habitat supports a fascinating array of insects. Our geographical position in the far South West gives us a much milder climate than the rest of the British Isles, particularly in winter – a critical benchmark for species establishing themselves as resident here.

The study of insects, or entomology, reveals a miniature world of drama and spectacle equal to any television wildlife epic, and all on our doorsteps. Sit down in any quiet spot during a hot, sunny day and you will hear the real soundtrack of summer, the rhythm of the natural world played out by insects. The gentle buzzing of bees, the fearsome clash of dragonfly wings, or grasshoppers stridulating during the heat of the day are all around us, yet we seldom notice them.

Some insects are regarded as pests, but many more are vital to the eco systems to which we ourselves belong. Without the many different insect pollinators, much of the plant life on which we all depend either directly, or indirectly, could not be sustained. Many species clear up much of the detritus, such as dung and carrion, which would otherwise clutter our crowded planet. When you step into their macro-world, many insects are incredibly beautiful, fantastically alien in design, amazingly intricate and perfectly evolved for their role on earth.

Insects (*Insecta*) are one of four classes of invertebrates that form the group known as *Arthropoda*, meaning 'jointed feet'. The other three classes include the *Arachnida* (spiders, mites, ticks and scorpions), *Myriapoda* (centipedes and millipedes) and *Crustacea* (crabs, lobsters, woodlice, etc).

Insects have their skeletons on the outside, largely formed from a substance called chitin

pocket
cornwall

Insects of Cornwall
and the Isles of Scilly

Steve Jones

Alison Hodge

First published in 2010 by
Alison Hodge, 2 Clarence Place, Penzance,
Cornwall TR18 2QA, UK
www.alison-hodge.co.uk
info@alison-hodge.co.uk

ISBN-13 978-0-906720-74-5

British Library Cataloguing-in-Publication Data
A catalogue record for this book is available from
the British Library.

Designed and originated by
BDP – Book Development and Production,
Penzance, Cornwall

Printed in China

Title page:
Common carder bee *(Bombus pascuorum)*

Acknowledgements
My sincere thanks are due to the following
for their help and advice during the prepara-
tion of this book: David Chapman for the
brown argus, holly blue, silver-washed fritillary
and weevil photographs; Adam Jones for the
Mother Shipton photograph; Bernard Hocking,
Leon Truscott, Lee Slaughter and Phil Boggis for
specialist advice, and Lynn Jones for proof-
reading my original text.

and protein, known as the cuticle, giving them a degree of armour plating. There is usually a covering of wax over the cuticle, which helps to waterproof the outer surface. This exoskeleton cannot expand, so in order to grow the insect must shed its skin, or moult, prior to becoming fully adult.

The body of an insect has three main sections: the head, thorax and abdomen.

The head includes the eyes, mouthparts and antennae. In addition to the two large, multi-faceted compound eyes that are extremely sensitive to movement, there are three very small, single-lens ocelli (simple eyes, consisting of a number of light-sensitive cells and a single lens), which are thought to be sensitive to light levels. The antennae are important sense organs which carry touch, heat, smell and humidity receptors.

The thorax is the middle section of the insect, which carries the legs and, if present, the two pairs of wings. Although some insects appear to have only one pair of wings, the second pair may be reduced to tiny stubs, as in some groups of flies. In others, such as beetles, it may be that one pair has evolved into a hard shell to protect the second pair of wings. The thorax itself is split into three sections. The upper surface of the first section, known as the pronotum, is often referred to

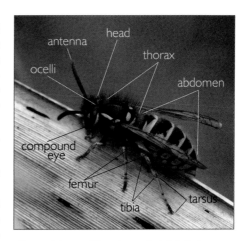

*The social wasp (*Vespula *species), labelled to show the main features of an insect's body*

in the description of identification features for specific species.

The abdomen is the tail section, and is usually divided into ten segments, those near the tip carrying the reproductive organs.

Insects are important parts of the food chain, either directly as prey items for small mammals and birds, or indirectly as pollinators of plant food sources. Many species of web-building spiders rely on flying insects as prey items; others, like the subtly camouflaged crab spider (*Misumena vatia*), lie in wait on flower heads, ready to pounce on unsuspecting pollen-feeders.

*The subtly camouflaged crab spider (*Misumena vatia*) lies in wait on a flower head, and pounces on unsuspecting pollen-feeders such as this Gatekeeper,* Pyronia tithonus

The Cornish climate is not always ideal for sun-loving insects, even during our summers. However, on cool, overcast days, insects such as dragonflies and moths are still able to take to the wing if they feel threatened. They do this by vibrating their wings in order to generate heat in the wing muscles through friction. After a short period of this 'wing-whirring' behaviour, the body temperature is elevated enough to enable flight.

The mining landscapes of Cornwall are an important habitat for many insects. The soils at such sites are often contaminated with heavy metals, which have retarded plant growth, leaving both terrestrial and aquatic habitats that are very open in nature, and which have persisted for many years.

Species such as the scarce blue-tailed damselfly (*Ischnura pumilio*) have benefited enormously from the wetland habitats of former tin-streaming valleys like the Red River valley near Camborne and the Carnon River valley above Devoran.

Burrowing insects such as solitary wasps and bees, and beetles such as the voracious green tiger beetle (*Cicindela campestris*) have also made use of the bare areas of mine waste to excavate their nest burrows.

Steve Jones, 2010

Insect-watching in the Field

Insect-watching is an activity best carried out on warm, sunny days. With a little care and effort most species are readily identifiable in their adult form. However, many insects are highly manoeuvrable and can be difficult to approach in the field, so a pair of close-focusing binoculars is very useful for obtaining critical views of important identification features.

When approaching insects, always remember that their compound eyes are extremely sensitive to movement. Therefore, approach your subject slowly and carefully, without making sudden movements, keeping your body as low as possible.

Occasionally, you may find an insect that puzzles you, and a casual glance from a distance is not sufficient to enable an accurate identification. In such circumstances it can be very useful to take a photograph so that you can study the insect closely at your leisure, often recording vital details that you might otherwise have missed. A digital single-lens reflex (SLR) camera with a macro lens is ideal for this; however, most compact cameras now have macro facilities and are very capable of producing good, clear images.

An SLR reveals the intricate details of a mayfly

(The Mother Shipton moth photograph on page 67 was taken with a compact camera.) Taking photographs such as the Mayfly on page 7 can be very rewarding, and provides the valuable opportunity of seeking a second opinion on identification at a later stage.

Carrying a clear plastic bug box with you when you are exploring the countryside is also useful, as some insects can be caught relatively easily and examined closely in the pot. A small hand lens is useful to magnify the details of your catch, although some bug boxes have magnifiers built into the lid for this purpose. Don't forget to release your catch back into its original habitat afterwards.

Insect-watching need not be confined to fine weather. For example, dragonflies emerging from their aquatic stage leave behind the cast skins of larvae (exuviae). These provide conclusive proof of which species are breeding at a site, and can be searched for in virtually any weather conditions. Although some exuviae are extremely difficult to identify, others are surprisingly easy with the aid of a x10 hand lens, or even with the naked eye. Collecting the abandoned exuviae can give a good indication of the size of a population at a site, and may also be the only clue to the presence of a species.

Remember to keep records of your sightings, such as when, where and which species you have seen, as such information can be invaluable to conservation organizations.

About this Book

This book gives an introduction to many of the more commonly occurring insects of Cornwall and the Isles of Scilly. Inevitably, it will only scratch the surface of such a vast subject, due to the constraints of space. However, at the back of the book (page 102) are references to the most authoritative guide for each group of insects, as well as contact details for specialists groups. The recording schemes run by these groups will welcome accurate observations and sightings from enthusiasts.

Although most of the species included here are a cross-section of those most commonly encountered, I have included some of the scarcer species of dragonflies and butterflies in order to give as complete a picture as possible for these two very popular and highly visible groups.

When describing the features that separate one similar species from another, I have not considered species that are presently unknown in Cornwall and the Isles of Scilly. Identification of insects beyond our borders is beyond the scope of this book!

When identifying insects, it is important to note that there are often a number of identical species separated only by the minutest of details, frequently visible only with a hand lens. In view of this, it is generally better to assume that the species you are looking at is the commoner one, until you can be certain otherwise. If you suspect that you have something unusual, consult a specialist text or group for confirmation.

An approximate gauge of size is important for some species, so for species such as the grasshoppers and crickets I have given body lengths (BL) from the head to the tip of the abdomen: for example, BL=23–33mm; for others, such as the dragonflies, I have given a wingspan (WS – wing tip to wing tip): for example, WS=65–73mm. Given that moths usually rest with their wings closed, rather than a wingspan the length of a single forewing (FW) is given: for example, FW=23–33mm. Note that even within the same species there is a variation in these sizes: females, for instance, are often larger than males; second broods are sometimes smaller than first broods, hence the range given in each case.

When commenting on the status and distribution of each species, I have used such terms as 'common' or 'widespread'. Unless otherwise stated, this refers to the whole of the area covered by this book, i.e. Cornwall and the Isles of Scilly. If a species does not occur on the Isles of Scilly, I have used the phrase 'Not IOS'.

Each species account has a calendar bar which shows when the adult insect is most likely to be seen (in dark green), and when early or late examples might be seen (in light green).

The Gazetteer (pages 95–7) lists some of the best sites for seeing insects, and is cross-referenced to individual species with a site number in red. Species that do not have these site numbers are so common that they may be seen virtually anywhere in the countryside.

Dragonflies and Damselflies

Dragonflies and damselflies are extremely beautiful insects which capture the very essence of summer as they perform their intricate aerobatics around the gleaming backdrop of rivers and pools on hot, sunny days. They are highly visible and important indicators of the health of our wetlands, being top insect predators as both airborne adults and aquatic larvae.

Dragonflies are entirely harmless and do not bite or sting (though they may give a gentle nip if roughly handled!). They also make superb subjects for photography, but getting close enough for a good shot can be difficult.

Over 40 species of Odonata (dragonflies) have been regularly recorded from the UK, and these can be divided into two sub-orders – the Zygoptera (damselflies) and the Anisoptera (dragonflies). Damselflies are generally smaller insects, which when at rest hold their wings together over their abdomen; obvious exceptions are the two species of emerald (*Lestes*) damselflies, which hold their wings out at 45 degrees to the abdomen when at rest. Dragonflies are generally larger insects, and as mature adults when at rest they hold their wings apart at approximately 90 degrees to their body.

Ten species of damselfly and 12 species of dragonfly have been reliably recorded as resident in Cornwall. Wetland habitats are very important for all Odonata species living in the county, with both dragonflies and damselflies spending the majority of their lives as larvae in a pond, river, lake or marsh. Without doubt, the legacies of Cornwall's once extensive mining industry have been a major source of prime dragonfly habitat. With very few exceptions, the sites which sustain the greatest diversity of species have been shaped by the search for tin or china clay, including areas such as the Red River Valley near Camborne, the Carnon Valley near Bissoe and Devoran, and the St Austell China Clay area/mid-Cornwall moors. The nationally rare scarce blue-tailed damselfly (*Ischnura pumilio*) has benefited enormously from the slow rate at which natural vegetation recolonizes such sites. Another nationally scarce insect, the small red damselfly (*Ceriagrion tenellum*), also flourishes at these sites where boggy pools have developed. One of Cornwall's more elusive dragonflies, the black-tailed skimmer (*Orthetrum cancellatum*), is another species which relies heavily on old mining sites, such as the shallow serpentine quarries of the Lizard peninsula and the china clay workings of the St Austell area.

Dragonflies first come to water as mature adults, the males establishing a territory along a stretch of freshwater habitat which they will defend against intrusion from other males, while also mating with any females that enter their domain. You may come across a male and female embraced in a heart shape: this is known as the 'wheel', a position which the pair adopt during copulation.

After mating, the female may lay her eggs in tandem with the male, the male grasping the female between the head and thorax with the tip of his abdomen. In dragonflies this tends to mean the pair fly low over the water and adopt a swinging motion so that the tip of the female's abdomen dips into the water with the eggs washing off randomly. In damselflies, where ovipositing is carried out in tandem, the male sometimes lowers the female down a plant stem so that she becomes totally immersed in the water before carefully depositing her eggs into the aquatic vegetation.

*A newly emerged keel skimmer (*Orthetrum coerulescens*)

In some species of dragonfly, where the female oviposits alone by dipping her abdomen into the water during flight, the male hovers nearby guarding against any rival male attempting to mate with her and displacing his sperm. (Males can remove another dragonfly's sperm before replacing it with their own).

Another strategy employed by some dragonfly and damselfly species involves the female ovipositing alone, by carefully placing her eggs in plant tissue with no male presence at all.

After the egg hatches, the larva may undergo as many as 15 moults over a period of one to two years or more before emerging as an adult. However, a species such as the red-veined darter (*Sympetrum fonscolombii*) can complete its larval stage in as little as three or four months, thus producing two generations in a year. At the other extreme, a golden-ringed dragonfly (*Cordulegaster boltonii*) may take up to five years to complete its larval development.

The transformation from aquatic larva to airborne adult is one of the most amazing spectacles in the natural world. In some species, such as the hawkers, this often happens during the early hours of the morning; other species, such as the darters, and most damselflies, continue to emerge throughout the day. In all Cornish species, the larvae select suitable, frequently vertical, plant stems to emerge on. Other species, not found in the county, such as the clubtails (*Gomphus* species), may emerge horizontally on a rock or bolder.

Once the larva is happy with its chosen emergence support, it remains in the same position for some time before the top of its thorax splits open and the adult slowly hauls itself out of the exuvia, head first. While its abdomen is still tucked in the exuvia, the fledgling adult hangs upside down, allowing its new legs to harden for about half an hour. It then miraculously flicks itself upwards, extracting the remainder of its abdomen while simultaneously grasping at a support with its newly hardened legs – a breathtaking manoeuvre which is all over in seconds. The insect then pumps up its wings and abdomen before allowing both to harden up. This whole process may take anything from two to three hours.

Emergence is a very vulnerable time for dragonflies, as while unable to fly they provide an easy meal for birds, spiders, slugs and ants. Deteriorating weather, such as rain showers or strong gusts of wind, can ruin a dragonfly's wings while they are relatively soft, leaving the insect flightless and doomed.

Newly emerged adults, known as tenerals, may fly well away from the wetland to feed and mature. It takes these tenerals several days to gain their full adult colours, and at this stage males frequently resemble females in tone. Once fully mature, the adult searches out suitable water bodies in order to breed. This may mean returning to the wetland where it developed as an aquatic larva, or it may involve a dispersal, with the obvious advantages of a winged adult allowing new sites to be colonized.

Populations of resident species are frequently reinforced by migrants from Europe, sometimes reaching our shores with spectacular non-resident species such as the scarlet darter (*Crocothemis erythraea*), the yellow-winged darter (*Sympetrum flaveolum*), and the vagrant emperor (*Anax ephippiger*). The most unexpected arrival to these shores must surely have been the green darner (*Anax junius*), which arrived from America on the tail of Hurricane Earl in September 1998. In recent years, only two migrant species have been recorded on a regular basis on the Cornish peninsula – the red-veined darter (*Sympetrum fonscolombii*), now reasonably well established on the Lizard as a semi-regular breeder, and the lesser emperor (*Anax parthenope*), which has gone from being unknown in Britain to becoming a regular sighting since 1996, particularly in East Cornwall.

*An emperor exuvia (*Anax imperator*)*

Beautiful Demoiselle

Calopteryx virgo

A very common, large (overall length 45mm), sturdy damselfly found on faster-flowing rivers and streams. The mature male is metallic blue-green with iridescent blue-brown wings which are lighter towards the tip and base. The female is metallic green with light yellowy-brown wings. In flight, the wings look fluttery like a butterfly. Often found a long way from flowing water, feeding along hedgerows, etc. A rare visitor to the IOS.

Banded Demoiselle

Calopteryx splendens

This species is restricted to the River Tamar and its tributaries, where it is fairly common and frequently occurs with the beautiful demoiselle. The metallic blue mature male has bands of blue-brown on each wing beyond the mid-line, with about a sixth of the wing clear at the tip and about half of the wing clear towards the base. The female is metallic green with light greenish wings. 15

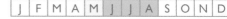

Emerald Damselfly

Lestes sponsa

The only resident damselfly in Cornwall to rest with its wings partly open at 45 degrees to the abdomen rather than together over its abdomen. Both sexes are metallic green; however, when mature, the blue-eyed male also has a blue pruinescence covering the first two and last two abdominal segments. Prefers shallow, lush pools where adults often roost in large numbers among the vegetation at the water's edge. WS=38mm. Not IOS. 4, 6, 7, 9, 11, 12, 14

White-legged Damselfly

Platycnemis pennipes

A distinctive, relatively large (WS=45mm) damselfly, with noticeably broad white legs at the tibia. While both sexes are creamy white when immature, the mature male has a vivid blue abdomen and the female a pale green abdomen. In Cornwall, this insect is restricted to areas of lush vegetation along unshaded, slower-flowing stretches of the River Tamar and its immediate tributaries. Not IOS. 15

| J | F | M | A | M | J | J | A | S | O | N | D |

| J | F | M | A | M | J | J | A | S | O | N | D |

Large Red Damselfly
Pyrrhosoma nymphula
Usually the first damselfly on the wing each year, exceptionally from mid-March. This very common red and black species has black legs, a feature which separates it from its smaller cousin, the small red damselfly, which has red legs. Numbers peak in May and June and decline dramatically through July and August. Common and widespread at garden ponds, pools and ditches. BL=36mm. Not IOS.

Small Red Damselfly
Ceriagrion tenellum
Nationally scarce, this species thrives in the wetlands that developed at old tin-streaming and china clay sites, and in the bogs, pools and seepages of Bodmin Moor. The male's abdomen is pure red, lacking the black markings of the large red with which it often occurs. The female's abdomen is usually at least 75 per cent black, but entirely red forms do occur. BL=31mm. Not IOS. 4, 9, 11, 12, 14

| J | F | M | A | M | J | J | A | S | O | N | D |

| J | F | M | A | M | J | J | A | S | O | N | D |

Azure Damselfly
Coenagrion puella

A common species throughout Cornwall, often flying with the similar common blue damselfly, from which it can be separated by the presence of a U-shaped mark on segment 2 of the abdomen. The underlying colour of the female is usually green, but may also be blue, though in both instances the insect appears to be rather more black when viewed from above. Seems to prefer smaller, well-vegetated ponds.

Common Blue Damselfly
Enallagma cyathigerum

A common insect, and the most likely damselfly to be found far out across open water in Cornwall. The male has a black 'mushroom' mark on segment 2 of the abdomen (near the thorax), which distinguishes it from the similar azure damselfly. When viewed from the side, both sexes have a single black stripe on the thorax, whereas the azure has one and a half. The background colour of the male is blue, the female can be a blue, green or straw colour.

| J | F | M | A | M | J | J | A | S | O | N | D |

Scarce Blue-tailed Damselfly
Ischnura pumilio
This nationally scarce insect prefers sites where there is a slight flow in shallow water over a silty bottom, with scant vegetation. Old tin-streaming valleys, flooded china clay pits, and moorland sites are ideal. The male has a black abdomen with a blue band near the tip covering part of segment 8 and all of segment 9. The immature female is initially a bright orange colour, maturing to a dull green with black along the upper surface of the abdomen. BL=29mm. Not IOS. 4, 14

Blue-tailed Damselfly
Ischnura elegans
A common and widespread insect that can tolerate mild pollution, and is often the only species present at a new pond. The male has a black abdomen, with a blue band near the tip confined to segment 8, as do immature females that have a reddy-pink or violet thorax. With maturity, the reddy-pink changes to yellowy-brown, and the violet to green or blue. All mature females have a light brown segment 8, except the blue form. BL=31mm.

J	F	M	A	M	J	J	A	S	O	N	D

J	F	M	A	M	J	J	A	S	O	N	D

Common Hawker
Aeshna juncea

A large, fast-flying insect (WS=95mm), the male is predominantly brown, yellow and blue; the female is brown and yellow. In flight, the side of the thorax appears to be mostly brown with broad yellow stripes, whereas the Southern hawker appears to be yellow/green with narrow brown stripes. A common species around moorland and heathland pools and old mining sites. Only found on Tresco in the Isles of Scilly. 4, 7, 11, 12, 14

Migrant Hawker
Aeshna mixta

This compact hawker (WS=85mm) is a relatively recent arrival that has steadily colonized Cornwall and the Isles of Scilly as a breeding species since the early 1990s. The migrant hawker has a prominent yellow T-shaped triangle on the second segment of the abdomen (near the thorax), which is absent in the larger common hawker. A non-aggressive species, widespread around still water habitats. 6, 7, 8

Male (left) and female (above)

thorax, which has two very broad disc-like markings rather than the thin, parallel stripes of the other two species. The last two pairs of spots at the tip of the abdomen are fused to form two bands, whereas in the common and migrant hawker both pairs remain separate. Common and widespread. 4, 6, 7, 9, 11, 12, 14

Southern Hawker
Aeshna cyanea
This large hawker (WS=100mm) is often very inquisitive, males repeatedly hovering close to the observer. The Southern hawker can be separated from both the common and migrant hawker by the upper surface of the

| J | F | M | A | M | J | J | A | S | O | N | D |

Emperor Dragonfly
Anax imperator

This striking insect is the largest resident species of dragonfly in Britain, with a wingspan of 106mm. It is widespread throughout Cornwall and the Isles of Scilly. The bright blue male tirelessly patrols large pools, swiftly seeing off rivals. The green female oviposits alone into aquatic vegetation close to the water surface. Both sexes have a green thorax.

Lesser Emperor Dragonfly
Anax parthenope

A very similar species to the emperor, and a regular immigrant to Cornwall which has successfully bred here. Both sexes have a brown thorax and a conspicuous yellow band around segment 2 of the abdomen, which the emperor lacks. The mature male generally has a green-brown abdomen with a distinctive blue band. WS=104mm.

| J | F | M | A | M | J | J | A | S | O | N | D |

| J | F | M | A | M | J | J | A | S | O | N | D |

Golden-ringed Dragonfly
Cordulegaster boltonii
The female, resplendent in its Cornish colours of black and gold, is one of the largest dragonflies in the UK, with an overall body length of 84mm, thanks to the unique, spike-like ovipositor on the end of its abdomen. This common and widespread insect breeds along rivers and streams, where the larval stage may last for up to five years. A rare visitor to the Isles of Scilly.

Four-spotted Chaser
Libellula quadrimaculata
This common and widespread species takes its name from the diagnostic spot in the middle of the leading edge of each of the four wings. Both sexes are brown, with yellow spots along the edge of the tapering, black-tipped abdomen. Often the most prolific species where it occurs, including heathland pools and old mining sites. Occasionally some specimens are found with extensive dark markings near the tip of the wings, a form known as *praenubila*. WS=75mm. Not IOS.

J	F	M	A	M	J	J	A	S	O	N	D

J	F	M	A	M	J	J	A	S	O	N	D

Broad-bodied Chaser

Libellula depressa

One of the first dragonflies on the wing each spring, it is also one of the first to colonize newly constructed garden ponds. Both sexes have pale shoulder stripes on the thorax and broad flat abdomens, blue in the male with yellow spots down each side, yellow in the female (see photo on page 104) and immature male. Both have extensive brown patches at the base of each wing (WS=76mm). Males often defend a territory from a prominent perch, to which they repeatedly return. Not IOS.

Black-tailed Skimmer

Orthetrum cancellatum

A characteristic species of flooded china clay pits, quarries, reservoirs and pools with bare margins where the males rest on the ground. This species has a low, rapid flight, appearing to almost glide at high speed with its wings up. Males have clear wings and blue abdomens with a noticeable black tip; females and immature males have yellow/tan abdomens with two black bands running throughout the entire length. WS=77mm. Widespread, but a rare visitor to the Isles of Scilly. 3, 6, 7

J	F	M	A	M	J	J	A	S	O	N	D

J	F	M	A	M	J	J	A	S	O	N	D

Common Darter
Sympetrum striolatum

A very common species, found at almost every standing water habitat throughout Cornwall and the Isles of Scilly. Often flies well into November and occasionally December, increasingly seeking out sunny spots well away from water. The male has an orangey-red abdomen; the female and immature males are a tan-brown colour. Both sexes have yellow patches on the side of the thorax. WS=58mm.

Keeled Skimmer
Orthetrum coerulescens

A small, slender dragonfly found at boggy seepages in heaths and moorlands, and shallow silty pools around old mining sites. The male has a pure blue abdomen; the female and immature male have a golden/tan abdomen. Both sexes have pale shoulder stripes on the thorax. Females have a yellow tinge to their wings; both sexes hold their wings forward (WS=60mm). Cornwall is a major stronghold for this insect. Not IOS. 4, 6, 9, 11, 14

Black Darter

Sympetrum danae

Confined to the moors and heathlands of East Cornwall, this small (WS=46mm), distinctive darter frequents shallow, boggy pools. The uniquely black male is unmistakable among the Cornish fauna, while the tan female and immature male can be distinguished by the presence of a black triangle on the top of the thorax. A restless species, making short, erratic flights. 12, 14

Red-veined Darter

Sympetrum fonscolombii

An annual summer immigrant from the Mediterranean region, which may turn up at any coastal site. Insects arriving early in the year often breed and produce a late-summer emergence of Cornish adults. A second, home-grown generation sometimes overwinter as larvae, emerging in May and June. The brick-red males have a red wash on their face (or frons), and varying numbers of red veins in the wings. The undersides of the eyes are always blue in both sexes. 6, 7

J	F	M	A	M	J	J	A	S	O	N	D

J	F	M	A	M	J	J	A	S	O	N	D

Grasshoppers, Crickets and Relatives

Grasshoppers, crickets and ground-hoppers all belong to the order Orthoptera (meaning 'straight wings'). They are usually grouped together with their close relatives the cockroaches (Dictyoptera), earwigs (Dermaptera) and stick-insects (Phasmida).

Only around 30 species of Orthoptera and their closely related relatives are regularly found in Cornwall, with perhaps a further 16 species having been recorded here in the past. The Orthoptera and their allies are therefore a nicely manageable group of insects to study, and with a little practice the common species are easily identified.

Grasshoppers, crickets and bush-crickets have enlarged hind legs with well-developed muscles that allow them to jump considerable distances. In some species, these hind legs also have a row of raised pegs on the inside of the widened femur which, during stridulation, are rubbed against a raised vein in the forewing to produce the distinctive songs.

The songs are a method of bringing the sexes together for mating, each species having its own unique song. Older observers may find it very difficult to hear these stridu-lations, but they can be picked up by a bat detector, which allows the identification of individual species from the song alone, without the need for actually seeing it.

The upper surface of the first segment of the thorax, known as the pronotum, is often an important feature in identifying grasshoppers, bush-crickets and ground-hoppers. The pronotum extends back over the top of the thorax, often covering the base of the wings, and has a variety of markings and ridges specific to individual species.

Colour is not a completely reliable method of identifying this group of insects, as shown by the pink example of the normally green meadow grasshopper (*Chorthippus parallelus*) on page 27.

In some species, such as the subterranean-dwelling mole cricket (now extinct in Cornwall), the front legs are greatly enlarged and widened as an adaptation for digging. Other species, such as the great green bush-cricket (*Tettigonia viridissima*), have hearing organs in the front legs.

Most Orthoptera pass through the winter in the egg stage, with the nymphs emerging in the spring. As the nymphs grow and moult, passing through as many as six instars, they become more and more like the fully grown adult, so for identification purposes it is important to determine that the specimen at hand is fully mature. The size of the wing buds is a good indicator of this. Like dragonflies, grasshoppers and crickets do not have a pupal stage.

Bush-crickets can be readily distinguished from grasshoppers by their extremely long antennae. Female bush-crickets also have long, scythe-like ovipositors lacked by grasshoppers. All of our grasshoppers are herbivores, whereas most of the bush-crickets are omnivorous.

Ground-hoppers are similar in appearance to grasshoppers. However, they are much smaller, and have very long pronotums which extend back over the entire length of the abdomen or beyond. Unlike their larger cousins, they may be seen in their adult form during most of the year.

Cockroaches are not necessarily the large, repellent insects found scuttling around commercial kitchens just before the health inspector closes down the establishment! Our native lesser cockroach (*Ectobius panzeri*) is a small (5–8mm), oval-shaped insect of dry heathland and coastal slopes.

Meadow grasshopper (Chorthippus parallelus)

Earwigs have large, distinctive pincers at the end of their abdomens, which despite appearances are harmless.

Stick-insects are, as their name suggests, long, thin, stick-like creatures that have become naturalized in Cornwall. Tresco in the Isles of Scilly, with its sub-tropical gardens of exotic plants, is particularly notable for stick-insects, with three species present: the prickly stick-insect (*Acanthoxyla geisovii*), the smooth stick-insect (*Clitarchus hookeri*), and the Mediterranean stick-insect (*Bacillus rossius*).

Great Green Bush-cricket
Tettigonia viridissima

This impressive insect is our largest species of Orthoptera (BL=40–54mm). A well-camouflaged species, generally green in colour, but has a tan stripe running the entire length of the upper surface of its head, pronotum and fully developed wings. Relatively common among tall vegetation along the coastal strip of both East and West Cornwall, it is also widespread inland throughout the latter. The loud stridulation is the classic soundtrack to a summer evening on the coast.

Dark Bush-cricket
Pholidoptera griseoaptera

Varying shades of brown give this insect its dark look when viewed from above; the underside is yellow/green. Relatively small (BL = 13–20mm), with very small forewings that do not extend beyond half-way along its abdomen; hindwings are absent in both sexes. Common along hedgerows, and in woodland and scrub clearings. No recent Isles of Scilly records. 5, 7, 8, 10, 17, 18

Grey Bush-cricket
Platycleis albopunctata

A grey/brown species with wings extending the full length of the abdomen. This medium-sized bush-cricket (BL = 20–28mm) is restricted to coastal habitats in Cornwall, including sand dunes, cliffs and shingle beach heads. Found only on Bryher in the Isles of Scilly. 1, 5, 8, 17

J	F	M	A	M	J	J	A	S	O	N	D

J	F	M	A	M	J	J	A	S	O	N	D

Bog Bush-cricket

Metrioptera brachyptera

One of Cornwall's rarest Orthoptera species, it is a key indicator of prime lowland heath. Generally green on the top of the head, pronotum and underside of the body; brown elsewhere. The side of the pronotum has a light band on the hind edge. BL=11–21mm. May be seen along the road crossing Rosenanon Downs, or the track across St Newlyn East Downs. Not IOS.

Long-winged Conehead

Conocephalus discolor

A relatively recent arrival in Cornwall and the Isles of Scilly, first recorded here in 1990. A small (BL=16–22mm), omnivorous species of warm, coarse grasslands, both sexes are generally green, with a golden-brown longitudinal stripe covering the wings and upper body surfaces. The wings extend beyond the tip of the abdomen. The female's ovipositor is straight. 1, 5, 6, 7, 9

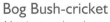

J F M A M J J A S O N D

J F M A M J J A S O N D

Short-winged Conehead

Conocephalus dorsalis

A small bush-cricket (BL=11–18mm), with the characteristically shaped 'cone' head which extends forwards and upwards to a point. This species normally has very short wings, which only reach about half-way along the abdomen, though long-winged forms do occasionally occur. The female's ovipositor is noticeably curved upwards. Seemingly absent from the far west and far north of the county, but widespread on the Isles of Scilly. 6

Speckled Bush-cricket

Leptophyes punctatissima

A small green bush-cricket (BL=9–18mm), covered in tiny dark spots. This speckled colouration, combined with the insect's slow movements, make it extremely well camouflaged and easy to overlook among bramble thickets. It has only very short forewings, and a complete absence of hindwings in both sexes. Relatively common and widespread along hedgerows, in scrub, woodland rides and gardens.

J	F	M	A	M	J	J	A	S	O	N	D

J	F	M	A	M	J	J	A	S	O	N	D

Cepero's Ground-hopper
Tetrix ceperoi

A nationally notable species, this small ground-hopper (BL=8–13mm) has some of its strongest populations in West Cornwall, particularly on the Lizard peninsula, where it may be found on wet, bare ground near pools and seepages. Two far more common ground-hoppers are found in Cornwall: the smaller, flightless common ground-hopper (*T. undulata*), in which the pronotum does not extend beyond the knees of the rear legs, and the slender ground-hopper (*T. subulata*), in which it does, as in Cepero's ground-hopper. Cepero's may be distinguished from the slender ground-hopper by the femur of the middle leg, which has a wavy outline rather than the relatively smooth outline of the latter. Not IOS. 5, 6, 8

Field Grasshopper
Chorthippus brunneus

A medium-sized (BL=15–25mm), fully winged grasshopper, uniquely distinguished by the noticeable abundance of fine, silvery hairs between the legs on the underside of the thorax (see below). Generally brown/tan in appearance, sometimes striped or mottled. Common in hot dry locations with low vegetation, along footpaths, cliffs, coastal slopes and dunes. It is the only resident grasshopper on the Isles of Scilly.

Meadow Grasshopper
Chorthippus parallelus

This very common, widespread medium-sized grasshopper (BL=15–22mm) is found in grasslands of all types. Mature adults are readily identifiable by the length of their wings, which usually fall well short of the tip of the abdomen in both sexes, though occasionally long-winged forms do occur. Generally green in colour, sometimes partly or wholly brown, with straight antennae. Occasionally vivid pink females may be found (as on page 27). Not IOS.

Mottled Grasshopper
Myrmeleotettix maculatus

A small grasshopper (BL=12–19mm) with clubbed antennae bent towards the tip in the male, and thickened antennae tips in the female. Generally grey-brown in colour, sometimes green, the insect frequently has extensive mottling over much of its body, providing an effective camouflage. Found on coastal sand dunes, dry heaths and derelict mining sites. A widespread species which can be locally numerous. Not IOS.

| J | F | M | A | M | J | J | A | S | O | N | D |

| J | F | M | A | M | J | J | A | S | O | N | D |

Common Earwig

Forficula auricularia

This is the largest of the three native species of earwig found in Cornwall and the Isles of Scilly, the overall lengths being 12.5–23mm for the common earwig, 8–10mm for Lesne's earwig, and 4.5–7mm for the lesser earwig. The female may lay up to 50 eggs, which she will then care for until after they have hatched and the nymphs have moulted for the first time. The mother will even lick the eggs to keep them mould-free. Common and widespread throughout the county, this insect is capable of flight but seldom takes to the air.

Unarmed Stick-insect

Acanthoxyla inermis

The most widespread of the five naturalized species of stick-insect occurring in Cornwall, though it is not recorded from the Isles of Scilly. Green or brown in colour (BL=94–125mm), this is the longest insect occurring in Cornwall and the UK. The relatively smooth body has a few small tubercules and a central black line running down the upper surface of the prothorax (just behind the head). Feeds on bramble, Banks' rose and potentilla. Originally a native of New Zealand and probably introduced through plant imports in the early 1920s.

| J | F | M | A | M | J | J | A | S | O | N | D |

| J | F | M | A | M | J | J | A | S | O | N | D |

True Bugs

Shield bugs, squash bugs, treehoppers, froghoppers, leafhoppers and aphids all belong to the order Hemiptera, with around 1,700 species occurring in Britain.

One of the notable features of bugs is that they all possess a beak, called the rostrum, which they use for piercing plants or other animals in order to extract juices or bodily fluids.

Although some species are wingless, bugs normally have two pairs of wings and, as with beetles, the forewings are usually hardened.

Bugs do not pass through a pupal stage, but grow as nymphs progressing through around five instars, subtly evolving at each moult towards the final adult form. It can be difficult to determine if you are looking at a nymph, or an adult of an entirely different species.

Bugs are divided into two sub-orders, the Heteroptera and the Homoptera. The Heteroptera have membranous tips to their hardened forewings, and rest with the wings held flat over the flattened body, as in a shield bug. The Homoptera hold their wings, if there are any, over the abdomen like a roof or tent, as in a froghopper. Homoptera species are entirely vegetarian, and some may cause serious damage to crops.

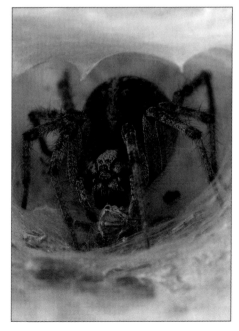

*A green leafhopper (*Cicadella viridis*) caught by a labyrinth spider,* Agelena labyrinthica

Hawthorn Shield Bug
Acanthosoma haemorrhoidale
As its name suggests, feeds on the leaves and fruit of the hawthorn, as well as other trees, such as oak, birch and hazel. BL = 14–17mm. The antennae are black and the distinctive, pointed lateral margins of the pronotum look like shoulder pads. Adults pass the winter in hibernation, but may sometimes be active in mild weather. A widespread insect found along hedgerows and woodland margins.

Green Shield Bug
Palomena prasina
One of several similar species that are common on trees and shrubs, often found in gardens. Eggs are laid in hexagonal batches in mid-summer, with the resulting adults overwintering in hibernation. Emerges from hibernation in May as a green adult, but in late autumn temporarily takes on a bronze appearance before entering hibernation again. Widespread but under-recorded. BL = 12–14mm.

| J | F | M | A | M | J | J | A | S | O | N | D |

| J | F | M | A | M | J | J | A | S | O | N | D |

Dock Bug
Coreus marginatus
There are a number of similar species, but the two small horns between the antennae are diagnostic of *C. marginatus*. Light brown with an oval-shaped abdomen, the whole body is speckled with tiny nodules throughout. Hibernates through the winter as an adult. Frequent and widespread, particularly along footpaths and hedgerows, often feeding on blackberries in the autumn. The larvae feed on dock. BL=13–15mm.

Froghopper
Cercopis vulnerata
A large, boldly coloured froghopper, BL=9–11mm. The nymphs live communally underground among solidified froth that they have produced around plant roots. Common in both wooded and open areas. One of a number of similar families of insects, froghoppers have just a few spines on the hind tibia, whereas leafhoppers have numerous spines, and planthoppers have a spur at the end of the hind tibia.

J	F	M	A	M	J	J	A	S	O	N	D

J	F	M	A	M	J	J	A	S	O	N	D

Common Froghopper
Philaenus spumarius

These jumping insects, also known as spittle-bugs, have nymphs that suck out sap from plants to produce the familiar masses of froth in which they live, commonly referred to as cuckoo spit. The adult is capable of jumping 70cm into the air – quite a feat for an insect that is only 5.5–6.5mm in length.

J	F	M	A	M	J	J	A	S	O	N	D

Butterflies

Butterflies are perhaps the most popular group of insects. Almost every part of our countryside has at least one of these colourful jewels dancing across the canvass of a perfect summer's day.

Around 40 species of butterflies are found regularly in Cornwall and the Isles of Scilly. Thirty-seven species have been resident since about the year 2000, and a further three species are regular immigrants that have produced a Cornish generation during the summer months.

Butterflies and moths both belong to the order Lepidoptera, and can often be confused with each other. Indeed, the scientific separation between the two is far from conclusive, but a few general observations may serve to separate the two groups. Butterflies have club-tipped antennae, whereas moths have a variety of different-shaped antennae, but not usually clubbed. Butterflies are generally day-flying insects, whereas moths are often nocturnal fliers. Butterflies usually rest with their wings closed vertically over their backs, while moths rest with their wings running along their body, or with the wings held out flat to the sides, forewings over hindwings in each case.

Unfortunately, there are a number of exceptions to each of these rules of thumb. A good example are the Burnett moths, which are day-flying and have clubbed antennae.

The intricate colour patterns of a butterfly are formed by numerous small scales of varying pigments, which cover the whole of the wing surface. These may easily be worn off if contact occurs, for example during mating. The surface of the scales often reflects light in different ways, according to their shape, so the colour of the butterfly can look vastly different depending on the angle from which it is viewed. An example is the purple hairstreak, which when viewed from the ground may look pinky-brown in colour, settled on the canopy of an oak, but appears to be purple and black in the hand.

The adult butterfly feeds through a tube known as a proboscis, with which it probes deep into a flower to get nectar. Uniquely in butterflies and moths, the proboscis is coiled up when not in use, as can be seen in the marsh fritillary (*Euphydryas aurinia*) on page 40.

Marsh fritillary (Euphydryas aurinia) showing coiled proboscis

In some species, the adult butterflies, or imagos, have front legs that are significantly smaller than the other legs. These are tucked up under the head, giving the impression that only four pairs of legs are present. In some species, the feet on these vestigial legs bear the taste organs.

Butterflies have scent organs in the antennae which allow the females to detect the larval food plant while in flight. They also have receptors in their feet which allow them to confirm that they have selected the right plant before egg-laying.

The four main stages in a butterfly's life cycle are the egg (or ovum), the caterpillar (or larva), the chrysalis (or pupa), and the adult butterfly (or imago).

The female lays large numbers of eggs, some of which will be eaten by predators or fall victim to parasites. Some species overwinter as eggs, but most hatch within a few weeks, at which time the larva eats its way out of the eggshell.

The larvae have a voracious appetite, and will moult three or four times in order to grow. When fully grown, the caterpillar stops feeding and looks for a suitable location to moult for the last time before pupating. Some species, such as the large white, overwinter as a chrysalis.

The caterpillar undergoes a complete metamorphosis inside the chrysalis, transforming and restructuring basic organs, and dissolving others that are no longer needed in order to provide the building blocks for any entirely new organs.

Shortly before the imago emerges from the chrysalis, the pattern and colour of the butterfly's wings can be seen through the pupal case. The butterfly breaks out by pressing its legs against the inside of the casing as the chrysalis splits behind the head. The newly emerged adult has crumpled wings, and is soft and flabby. Fluids are pumped from the body to expand the wings until they reach their full extent. The butterfly remains motionless while the wings harden ready for flight.

This flying adult stage allows the species to disperse, perhaps colonizing new sites many miles away, to seek a mate and to lay eggs.

Migrating species such as the painted lady can travel hundreds of miles in large numbers to colonize new areas. In April 2009, there was a large migration of this species from North Africa up into Spain and Portugal, giving rise to an Iberian generation which in turn moved north to Cornwall and the UK. By mid-summer there were thousands of painted lady caterpillars feeding on thistles throughout the county, giving us our own Cornish generation.

Many butterflies have suffered serious declines over the last few decades, and species such as the pearl-bordered fritillary have been reduced to just a few scattered populations. Others, such as the large blue and the heath fritillary, have at various times become extinct in the county, though fortunately both have been the subject of successful reintroductions.

Grizzled Skipper

Pyrgus malvae

A notable species, this little brown and white/cream butterfly (WS = 23–29mm) has a more chequered appearance on all four wings than the superficially similar dingy skipper. The adults like to bask on bare surfaces in sunny, sheltered habitats where the larval food plants include wild strawberry. Sadly, the species is now reduced to just two known sites in Cornwall: the coastal dunes at Penhale, and old railway-track beds on the edge of Goss Moor. Not IOS. 8, 11

Dingy Skipper

Erynnis tages

Easily overlooked, this small brown species (WS = 26–34mm) often basks on bare ground where older examples are well camouflaged. Fresh specimens are much more vivid, having intricate grey markings. Normally there is only a single generation each year; however, in favourable conditions there is a second brood in August. Both adults and larvae feed on bird's-foot trefoil. Widespread but not at all common, it occurs at old mining sites and quarries, on heaths and coastal grasslands. Not IOS. 4, 8, 11, 18

Small Skipper
Thymelicus sylvestris

A distinctive little golden-orange butterfly (WS=27–34mm) that holds its forewings directly above its hindwings at an angle of about 30 degrees when basking. The male can be distinguished from the female by the presence of a dark diagonal line of scent scales on the forewing. It is only marginally smaller than the large skipper, with which it sometimes occurs. Common in areas of rough grassland, woodland margins and coastal slopes. Not IOS.

Large Skipper
Ochlodes venata

Easily confused with the very similar small skipper, the orange forewings of the large skipper have varying degrees of brown patterning anchored towards the hind margins, which are absent in the former. The black scent scales on the male's forewing are more prominent than those of the small skipper. WS=29–36mm. Common in areas of rough grassland, woodland margins and coastal slopes. Not IOS. 9

J	F	M	A	M	J	J	A	S	O	N	D

J	F	M	A	M	J	J	A	S	O	N	D

Large White
Pieris brassicae

Commonly known as a cabbage white, this large butterfly is regarded as a garden pest because of the damage it causes to cruciferous plants. Apart from being larger than the very similar small white, it generally has black markings on the edge of the forewing that extend equally in both directions from the apex. In the small white, these black markings generally only extend along the leading edge of the wing. Common, with summer numbers swollen by migrants from Europe.

Small White
Pieris rapae

A very common medium-sized butterfly (WS=38–55mm) that is likely to be encountered anywhere, with numbers reinforced each year by migrants. Lacks the prominent vein patterning of the green-veined white, and is less heavily marked at the apex of the forewing than the large white. Along with its larger cousin, the small white is considered to be a horticultural pest, the larvae feeding on crucifers such as cabbages.

Green-veined White
Pieris napi

Very similar to both the large and the small white. However, unlike those two species the green-veined white has extensive, well-defined green or grey vein patterns on the undersides of the wings, and is not a garden pest. A relatively common butterfly around woodland margins, hedgerows and scrub that has two generations a year, the wing markings in the spring population being paler than in the second generation. 11, 18

Orange Tip
Anthocharis cardamines

Only the male has the distinctive orange wing tips, but both sexes have very rounded wing tips and a mottled goldie-green and white underside to the hind wings. The female frequently lays its eggs on the cuckoo flower. Only one egg is laid per flower-head, due to the larvae being cannibalistic. Common in damp meadows, hedgerows and woodland clearings, the species is a real sign of spring. Not IOS. 11, 12

| J | F | M | A | M | J | J | A | S | O | N | D |

| J | F | M | A | M | J | J | A | S | O | N | D |

Brimstone
Gonepteryx rhamni
The striking yellow male brimstone was perhaps the original 'butter-coloured fly', which
later became the 'butterfly'. The less showy
female is a greenish-white; both sexes have a
small orange dot on each wing. During hibernation, the large, sculpted wings are closed,
providing effective leaf-like camouflage.
Widespread in woodland clearings of East
Cornwall, much scarcer west of Truro, along
with its larval food plant the alder buckthorn.
Rare on the Isles of Scilly. 12, 16, 18

Clouded Yellow
Colias croceus
A migrant from the Mediterranean region of
Europe and North Africa that has occasionally overwintered here in recent years. This
large (WS=45–54mm), vivid yellow butterfly, with noticeably pink wing fringes, legs and
antennae, tends to rest with its wings closed.
Most likely to be encountered near the coast,
but in good years it could turn up anywhere.
5, 17

| J | F | M | A | M | J | J | A | S | O | N | D |

| J | F | M | A | M | J | J | A | S | O | N | D |

Small Tortoiseshell
Aglais urticae

One of our best-known butterflies, sadly this beautiful visitor to our gardens has declined in numbers in recent years, though it remains widespread. Occurs in almost any open habitat, and may be seen throughout the year. Adults may be found hibernating in garages and sheds, and are sometimes tempted to fly on warmer winter days. The undersides of the wings are black-brown with pale markings towards the outer edges. WS=47–61mm. The black and yellow larvae feed on nettles.

Comma
Polygonia c-album

A highly recognizable butterfly, due to the scalloped outline of its wings. This medium-sized species takes its name from the white comma-shaped mark on the underside of its hindwings. Usually found along woodland rides, the comma is also attracted to gardens and is a widespread species. There are two generations a year, the first produced from eggs laid by overwintering adults in the spring. The larvae frequently feed on nettles. 12, 18

| J | F | M | A | M | J | J | A | S | O | N | D |

| J | F | M | A | M | J | J | A | S | O | N | D |

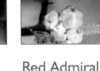

Painted Lady
Vanessa cardui

A large, attractive migrant butterfly from North Africa, which sometimes reaches our shores in its thousands from staging posts in southern Europe. Both sexes are orangey-brown overall, with white spots among the irregular black-brown markings of the fore-wing. WS=54–65mm. Early summer arrivals give rise to a Cornish generation later in the year, when the larvae can be found on thistles. Likely to occur in almost any sunny locality.

Red Admiral
Vanessa atalanta

This large, unmistakable velvety black and red butterfly (WS=56–68mm), is primarily a migrant to our shores, though it does breed here and may also overwinter on the Isles of Scilly in favourable conditions. It is frequently attracted to buddleia in the summer, and ivy blossom in the autumn, as well as over-ripe fruit. Likely to occur in almost any sunny locality. Larvae from the summer brood may be found on nettles.

| J | F | M | A | M | J | J | A | S | O | N | D |

| J | F | M | A | M | J | J | A | S | O | N | D |

Peacock
Inachis io

One of our best-known species, frequently attracted to gardens where it often feeds on buddleia and hibernates in our sheds and garages. A large butterfly (WS=63–75mm), with very impressive eyespots on the upper wings to startle would-be predators contrasting sharply with the predominantly black underside, which provides good camouflage for the hibernating insect. Capable of producing a hissing noise by rubbing its wings together to deter would-be predators.

Silver-washed Fritillary
Argynnis paphia

Named after the silvery bands on the undersides of the hindwings, this strong-flying, bright orange butterfly is our largest resident fritillary (WS=60–76mm). The female is generally a duller orange than the male; however, a bronze-green female colour form, *valezina*, may occasionally be seen. A sun-loving insect, it is relatively common in the sheltered, wooded valleys of East Cornwall, less so in West Cornwall. The larvae feed on dog violets. Not IOS. 13, 16, 18

| J | F | M | A | M | J | J | A | S | O | N | D |

| J | F | M | A | M | J | J | A | S | O | N | D |

Dark Green Fritillary
Argynnis aglaja
The upper sides of the wings of this large butterfly (WS= 58–68mm) are a typical orange and black check pattern common to many fritillaries; however, the underside of the hindwing has distinctive silver spots set against a green background. Generally found on coastal grassland and dunes, where it feeds on thistles and knapweed, this powerful flyer also occurs in woodland clearings. Not IOS. 1, 2, 8, 13, 18

Pearl-bordered Fritillary
Boloria euphrosyne
One of our most threatened species, having declined in Cornwall due to habitat degradation. In addition to the row of seven white 'pearls' running along the edge of the underside of the hindwing, which both the pearl-bordered and the small pearl-bordered have, the former has two additional 'pearls', whereas the later has a further eight or more. WS=44–47mm. Found along woodland edges and clearings, and sheltered coastal valleys, the larvae feed on dog violets. Not IOS. 13, 18

Small Pearl-bordered Fritillary
Boloria selene

A relatively small (WS=36–42mm), orange-brown fritillary. This species has more black on the underside of its wing than the similar, but larger, pearl-bordered fritillary. A widespread butterfly throughout the county, it can be found along our coastal fringes, on open heathland and in damp woodland. Frequently has two generations a year, with a lull between the two during late July and early August. 1, 2, 5, 6, 11, 12, 13, 16, 18

Heath Fritillary
Mellicta athalia

One of the UK's rarest butterflies, Cornish populations are restricted to a few woodland clearings along the Tamar valley. The decline of coppicing is thought to have led to the demise of this species, sometimes referred to as the 'woodman's follower'. A relatively small species (WS=39–45mm), with extensive brown areas near the base of the wings. Larval food plants include common cowwheat and ribwort plantain. Not IOS. 16

| J | F | M | A | M | J | J | A | S | O | N | D |

| J | F | M | A | M | J | J | A | S | O | N | D |

Marsh Fritillary

Euphydryas aurinia

One of our most threatened species, having suffered a dramatic decline nationally in recent years. The larvae construct a dense web around their food plant, devil's-bit scabious, where they live and feed as a group, relocating to a new plant after the first is consumed. Usually associated with open areas in wet heathland and marshy grassland where tussocks occur. WS=30–46mm. Not IOS. 6, 12

Marbled White

Melanargia galathea

A large, striking black and white butterfly (WS=46–58mm), which frequents tall unimproved grasslands, including coastal slopes, meadows and occasionally roadside verges. Adults feed on thistles, knapweed and scabious. The female lays its eggs in flight, which then fall randomly. A widespread and locally common insect in East Cornwall, but absent from West Cornwall and the Isles of Scilly. 10, 16, 18

Grayling
Hipparchia semele

This widespread species is often overlooked, due to its habit of settling on bare ground for extended periods. With wings closed, the butterfly often leans to one side, allowing the camouflage of the marbled grey, white and black hind underwing to have maximum effect. When disturbed, it flashes the eyespot on the forewing. Favours dry, open habitats such as old mining sites, stone quarries and heathlands. WS=51–60mm. Not IOS. 1, 5, 7

Meadow Brown
Maniola jurtina

A common and numerous species along woodland rides and clearings, on hedgerows and roadside verges, and in grassy meadows. The female may be confused with the smaller gatekeeper, which generally has more orange on the upper surface of the hindwing. The Isles of Scilly population belongs to a separate subspecies, *cassiteridum*, which generally has less spots on the underside of the wings than the mainland populations. WS=40–60mm.

J	F	M	A	M	J	J	A	S	O	N	D

J	F	M	A	M	J	J	A	S	O	N	D

Gatekeeper

Pyronia tithonus

Sometimes known as the hedge brown, the gatekeeper is a medium-sized butterfly (WS=34–38mm) that has orange wings with broad brown margins. Very common and frequently abundant species in grasslands, open woodland rides and hedgerows. Often seen with the meadow brown from which it differs by usually having two white markings in the black eyespot, rather than the one of the latter. Not IOS.

J	F	M	A	M	J	J	A	S	O	N	D

Ringlet

Aphantopus hyperantus

A chocolate-brown butterfly which takes its name from the series of black eyespots, ringed in yellow with white centres, on the underside of all four wings. WS=42–52mm. A common and widespread species, often found along hedgerows, in domestic gardens and churchyards, and in woodland clearings and edges, where the butterfly feeds extensively on bramble blossom. Can sometimes be found flying in light rain. Not IOS.

J	F	M	A	M	J	J	A	S	O	N	D

Small Heath

Coenonympha pamphilus

A small, orangey-brown butterfly which usually rests with its wings closed, the underside of the forewing having a small black eyespot ringed in yellow. WS=33–37mm. Adults nectar on flowers such as thistles and knapweeds. The eggs are laid singly on grasses. Has two generations a year. Widespread in grassy areas including coastal slopes, moorland, heathland and meadows. A rare migrant to the Isles of Scilly. 1, 8, 12

Speckled Wood

Pararge aegeria

This medium-sized (WS=38–44mm) butterfly is one of our most abundant species. Woodland clearings and almost every lane, bridleway or footpath with well-developed hedgerows will have at least one speckled wood making frequent short flights in the dappled light. The Isles of Scilly have a subspecies, *insula*, which has larger dots that are orange rather than the straw-yellow of the Cornish mainland populations.

| J | F | M | A | M | J | J | A | S | O | N | D |

| J | F | M | A | M | J | J | A | S | O | N | D |

Wall Brown

Lasiommata megera

A sun-loving, medium-sized butterfly (WS=44–50mm), which can frequently be found basking on bare ground, stony banks and walls. The orange and brown wall looks superficially like a fritillary, but unlike that group of butterflies it has one eyespot on each forewing, and three or more on each hindwing. A widespread species in Cornwall, particularly around the coastal strip, but only an occasional visitor to the Isles of Scilly. Has two generations a year. 1, 2, 3, 5

Purple Hairstreak

Quercusia quercus

An elusive small butterfly (WS=24–28mm) that lives in the canopy of oak trees, where it may be seen flitting between the leaves in the early evening. Adults occasionally found at ground level, visiting the fruits and flowers of brambles. Named from the distinctive purplish-blue iridescence on the upper surfaces of the forewing; however, the patches vary in size, and the colour can look very different depending on the angle from which the insect is viewed, at times appearing to be a pinky-grey colour. Widespread in East Cornwall, scarcer in the west. Not IOS. 9, 18

| J | F | M | A | M | J | J | A | S | O | N | D |

| J | F | M | A | M | J | J | A | S | O | N | D |

Green Hairstreak

Callophrys rubi

A very striking small butterfly (WS=26–30mm) that holds its wings closed when at rest, displaying the vivid iridescent green of the underside. Despite this, it is a difficult species to spot as it merges so well with surrounding vegetation. More likely to be encountered along the gorsy coastal fringes of Cornwall, but can also be found on heath and moorlands inland as well as in old quarries. Not IOS. 10, 12, 17

Small Copper

Lycaena phlaeas

An eye-catching little copper-orange butterfly. The sexes are very similar in appearance, but the female has slightly more rounded wings. WS=26–35mm. Look out for the attractive colour form *caeruleopunctata*, which has a row of blue spots set just above the orange band at the rear of the otherwise brown hindwings. Common along woodland rides, open meadows, coastal strips and larger gardens. Not IOS. 1, 2, 3, 5, 8, 9, 10, 11, 12, 16

| J | F | M | A | M | J | J | A | S | O | N | D |

| J | F | M | A | M | J | J | A | S | O | N | D |

Holly Blue

Celastrina argiolus

This is the blue species most likely to be encountered in domestic gardens. Unlike the other blues, the undersides of the wings are a very pale blue, and simply marked with black spots. In some years it is badly affected by a wasp parasitizing the larvae, which causes a dramatic crash in numbers. There are two generations a year: spring eggs are laid on holly, summer eggs on ivy. Widespread in woodland, churchyards and hedgerows. 18

Silver-studded Blue

Plebejus argus

One of our more notable butterflies, the ground-colour of the female is brown; that of the male is blue. In both sexes the underside of the hindwing has black spots centered with metallic blue studs set between an orange band and the wing edge, which are absent in the common blue. WS=26–32mm. Found in coastal habitats such as sand dunes and heathlands. Not IOS. 2, 3, 8, 12

J	F	M	A	M	J	J	A	S	O	N	D

J	F	M	A	M	J	J	A	S	O	N	D

Brown Argus

Aricia agestis

Classified as a 'blue', both male and female are brown with a band of orange markings near the edge of the upperside of each wing, as per the female of the common and silver-studded blue. Unlike these females, it usually has no blue scales on the upperside of its wings, but may have a blue sheen. Generally found along the north coast of West Cornwall; strong populations at Penhale Sands and Upton Towans. Not IOS. 2, 8

J	F	M	A	M	J	J	A	S	O	N	D

Common Blue

Polyommatus icarus

The most common and widespread of our blues, this small (WS=28–36mm), attractive butterfly is found on each of the main islands in the Isles of Scilly. The male is blue, the female brown. In dull weather, adults can be found roosting head down on grass stems. The common blue favours open habitats, including coastal fringes, sand dunes, grassy meadows and heathland, where the larvae feed on bird's-foot trefoil.

J	F	M	A	M	J	J	A	S	O	N	D

Moths

There are over 2,400 species of moths that are known to occur in Britain, many with beautiful patterns and designs the equal of any butterfly. Nearly 900 of these species are popularly known as 'macro moths', these generally being the larger species. The remaining species, usually within a fore-wing length of less than a centimetre, are collectively known as 'micro moths'. With the exception of the plume moth, the examples that follow are macro moths.

It is a popular misconception that moths fly only at night. In fact, a number of species fly during the day. Anyone who has visited one of Cornwall's sand-dune complexes will be familiar with the huge numbers of six-spot burnet moths that are active throughout the day.

Many night-flying moths are attracted to lighted windows at night, and those with an interest in moths (lepidopterists) use this apparent disorientation in order to trap them. Specialist moth traps with mercury vapour lamps are run at night, and any moths flying to the light are funneled into a box, often lined with old egg trays, where the insect will settle in the pockets of shade. Later in the evening, or the next the morning, the contents of the box are examined and identified before the moths are released completely unharmed. An organized moth evening of this kind is a great way to learn more about the subject.

Although moths are harmless, some people express a fear of them, perhaps because of their crazed flight when mesmerized by a light, or sometimes because of the big feathery antennae possessed by a number of species. Only the male has these elaborate antennae, with their increased surface area, which he uses to pick up the female's scent in the search for a mate.

Like butterflies, moths belong to the order Lepidoptera. The division between the two sets of insects is not a truly scientific one; however, I have outlined the general differences in the butterfly section (page 39). One additional feature of many moths, which butterflies do not have, is a wing-connecting bristle known as the 'frenulum'. The frenulum grows from the base of the hindwing, and attaches into a hook on the forewing connecting the two wings together.

White Plume
Pterophorus pentadactyla

An unmistakable micro moth that has wings divided into five feathery sections on each side. When at rest, with its wings folded together, the whole insect forms a T-shape. Frequently seen around the coastal strip and along hedgerows, the white plume is probably widespread but under-recorded, particularly in the north-east of the county. There are other similar plume moths, but none of them are white. 8

Six-spot Burnet
Zyganea filipendulae

A colourful, day-flying moth of coastal grasslands and dunes; also along roadside verges, on downland and in woodland clearings, where the larval food plant bird's-foot trefoil grows. Close examination towards the tip of the forewing shows two red spots rather than the one of the very similar five-spot burnet. The pairs of red spots are sometimes fused, and the two at the base of the forewing are separated only by a vein. 2, 3, 5, 8

J	F	M	A	M	J	J	A	S	O	N	D

J	F	M	A	M	J	J	A	S	O	N	D

Oak Eggar

Lasiocampa quercus

A large, heavy-bodied moth (FW=25–40mm), widespread on heathland, coastal dunes and woodland margins. The buff-coloured female flies and lays its eggs during the night; however, the brown male, with its feathery antennae, is a rapid daytime flier. Both sexes have a wavy yellow band across the forewing, with a white spot towards the centre of the wing. The larval food plants include heathers, bramble and hawthorn. 13

Elephant Hawkmoth

Deilephila elpenor

A large, pink and olive-green moth (FW=28–33mm) that may be seen feeding on honeysuckle at dusk. Its smaller cousin, the small elephant hawkmoth (*D. porcellus*), is very similar, but pink and yellowish-brown in colour. The equally striking caterpillar looks a little like an elephant's trunk, and often feeds on rosebay willow-herb. A common species of gardens, hedgerows, heathlands and sand dunes.

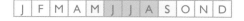

Hummingbird Hawkmoth
Macroglossum stellatarum

As it darts and hovers in front of flowers, with its rapid wing beats giving off a discernible hum, it is not difficult to see why this day-flying moth may be mistaken for its avian namesake. The species sometimes overwinters here, but the majority are migrants from southern Europe and North Africa, and can be found throughout the county in good years, where the adult is particularly attracted to buddleia, valerian and foxgloves.

Buff-tip
Phalera bucephala

With its grey wings held close to the body, contrasting to the prominent buff-coloured thorax and wing tips, the buff-tip looks remarkably like a broken twig. Often found in gardens, hedgerows and woodland, this large moth (FW=22–34mm) is readily attracted to well-lit windows at night. A common and widespread species, the larvae feed on a wide variety of broad-leaved trees.

J	F	M	A	M	J	J	A	S	O	N	D

J	F	M	A	M	J	J	A	S	O	N	D

Garden Tiger

Arctia caja

This striking insect is the most commonly seen of the tiger moths. The hindwings are a vivid orange with dark blue spots, and are normally hidden; if disturbed the insect displays them as a warning to predators. Larvae are very hairy, black and red-brown, sometimes known as woolly bears, and feed on common nettles and docks. Widely distributed in open habitats: gardens, scrubby sand dunes, meadows and woodland clearings. 8

Cinnabar

Tyria jacobaeae

The cinnabar moth is similar in overall colouration to the six-spot burnet, but each forewing has a pinky-red leading edge and two pinky-red dots at the hind margin. The larvae are much more likely to be encountered, and feed extensively on common ragwort, often reducing the plant to a bare stem. Widespread in coastal sand dunes, short-cropped grassland and heathland. FW=17–23mm.

| J | F | M | A | M | J | J | A | S | O | N | D |

| J | F | M | A | M | J | J | A | S | O | N | D |

Rosy Footman
Miltochrista miniata

An unmistakable species with vivid orangey-pink wing margins and distinctive, fine black wavy lines across the forewings. Often found around woodland and tree-lined hedgerows where the larvae feed on lichens. This widespread species readily comes to the light at night. FW=12–15mm.

Four-spotted Footman
Lithosia quadra

A nationally scarce insect with good populations in Cornwall and the Isles of Scilly, it is twice the size of any other British footman. The adult flies both during the day and the night. The larvae feed on lichen and algae growing on oaks and other broadleaved trees. Only the female has the two diagnostic spots on each wing; the male is distinguished by the dark marking at the base of the forewing's leading edge.

| J | F | M | A | M | J | J | A | S | O | N | D |

| J | F | M | A | M | J | J | A | S | O | N | D |

Angle Shades

Phlogophora meticulosa

A distinctive species found almost anywhere in Cornwall and the Isles of Scilly throughout the year, frequently in gardens. Wing colours vary a little, with the brown markings on the wings of this individual being replaced by green, particularly in fresh examples. The pattern remains constant, however. A night-flying moth, but often seen in the day at rest in prominent positions. FW=21–25mm.

Gold Spot

Plusia festucae

This beautifully patterned species can be recognized by the two bold silver marks in the middle of each of the forewings and a third, slightly less well-defined, silver wedge-shaped mark towards the rear edge of the wing. The larvae feed on rushes, sedges and course grasses associated with damp areas such as marshes, wet heathlands and rushy meadows. Widespread. FW= 14–19mm. 4

J	F	M	A	M	J	J	A	S	O	N	D

J	F	M	A	M	J	J	A	S	O	N	D

Silver Y
Autographa gamma

An annual migrant from southern Europe that often reaches our shores in very large numbers. A restless day- and night-flying species that rarely allows a close approach before whirring its wings and taking flight. A number of similar species also have the white/silver Y-shaped mark on the forewings, but the stalk is often separate from the rest of the 'Y' in those species. May turn up almost anywhere. FW = 15–20mm.

Mother Shipton
Callistege mi

The forewings of this common moth have a pattern that resembles the distinct outline of an old croan's face with an eye, hooked nose and protruding chin. With this in mind, it was named after the infamous Yorkshire witch, Old Mother Shipton. A day-flying moth found in grassy areas, where the larvae feed on clovers and trefoils. FW = 13–16mm. 12

| J | F | M | A | M | J | J | A | S | O | N | D |

| J | F | M | A | M | J | J | A | S | O | N | D |

Herald
Scoliopteryx libatrix

An attractive species with strongly sculpted trailing edges to the forewings, this medium-sized moth (FW=19–23mm) overwinters as a hibernating adult, often in outbuildings. A widespread species throughout Cornwall and the Isles of Scilly, the larvae feed on sallows and willows. Also known as the furbelow moth by some early naturalists, presumably after the frilly or pleated edge of a woman's dress, which was also known as the furbelow.

Early Thorn
Selenia dentaria

A distinctive species; rests with wings closed upright over its body like a butterfly, resembling a dead leaf. Two generations a year, the summer brood being smaller than the spring. The larvae are twig-mimics feeding on hawthorn, birch and other small trees and shrubs. Common in woodland, hedgerows and gardens; often attracted to house lights at night.

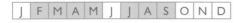

J	F	M	A	M	J	J	A	S	O	N	D

J	F	M	A	M	J	J	A	S	O	N	D

True Flies

True flies belong to the order Diptera, and are a huge collection of flying insects that have evolved so that their hindwings are reduced to vestigial, drumstick-like, balancing appendages known as halteres, leaving them with a single pair of forewings for flight. The larvae can be either terrestrial or aquatic, and are legless.

Flies feed mainly on liquids, and have mouth parts adapted for sucking, or piercing and sucking. Hoverflies suck up nectar, for example, while mosquitoes and horse-flies suck up blood, having first pierced their victim's skin. Species such as the house-fly regurgitate digestive fluids on to their food source in order to reduce solids to liquid form prior to sucking them up. When this is done in a domestic setting, there are obviously health issues for humans.

This order includes the rather fragile-looking crane-flies or daddy-long-legs that are the flying adult forms of the leatherjackets so despised by gardeners.

Because of the brevity of this book, and in order to limit the sections to a manageable number, I have placed three insects at the

*A recently emerged green bottle (*Lucilia sericata*) feeding on a blackberry*

end of this section that do not belong to the order Diptera. These are the stonefly which belongs to the order Plecoptera , a small group of insects rarely seen far from water; the alderfly belonging to the order Neuroptera (meaning 'nerve-winged'), and the scorpion-fly that belongs to the order Mecoptera, which has only four British species.

Dotted Bee-fly
Bombylius discolor

This nationally scarce insect looks like a tiny (BL=8–13mm) bumblebee. But at rest, the stance of its wings and body give it a triangular appearance, and this is tipped by an extremely long proboscis. Bee-flies are harmless, and use their long proboscis to probe for nectar as they hover in front of flowers, emitting a high-pitched whine. Most likely to be seen on the Lizard peninsula. Not IOS. The more common dark-edged bee-fly (*B. major*) does not have the prominent dark brown dots at the junctions of the wing veins.

Noon Fly
Mesembrina meridiana

A distinctive black species of fly with bright orange flashes towards the base of each wing, an orangey-yellow face, and orange tips to the claws at the tip of the tarsi. Often found on umbellifers, or sunbathing on bare ground near rivers, hedgerows, and along the coastal strip. The female lays its eggs in dung, where the larvae will feed. Common but under-recorded, and not currently noted from the Isles of Scilly.

Hoverfly

Episyrphus balteatus

A distinctive and very common little hoverfly. Markings on the abdomen are variable, but those on the upper surface of segments (or tergites) 3 and 4 always have double black bands of varying boldness. The upper surface of the thorax is also distinctive, in having a faint narrow grey stripe in the centre, flanked by a slightly broader grey stripe on either side of it. Abundant in gardens, with numbers boosted by migrants.

Hoverfly

Xanthogramma pedissequum

A low-flying insect that is attracted to low-growing flowers in grassland areas. Distinctive in having two yellow equilateral triangles on the margins of tergite 2, and wings which have dark smudges half-way along the leading edge. Stands out as being a very sulphur-yellow, contrasting sharply with a strong, glossy black. The larvae feed on aphids. Widespread but not particularly common. Not IOS.

Hoverfly
Volucella pellucens

Frequently found on bramble flowers, this very large black hoverfly is readily identified by tergite 2 of the abdomen being white. Often found in woodland clearings, the adults are said to enter wasps' nests without being attacked, in order to lay their eggs, with the larvae subsequently living there. Widespread throughout Cornwall and the Isles of Scilly.

Drone Fly
Eristalis tenax

This large hoverfly closely mimics male hive bees or drones, hence its English name. The abdominal pattern is variable, but the species can be separated from the very similar *E. pertinax* by its dark front tarsi as opposed to the light front tarsi of the latter. The aquatic larva is sometimes known as the rat-tailed maggot. Very common throughout Cornwall and the Isles of Scilly.

| J | F | M | A | M | J | J | A | S | O | N | D |

| J | F | M | A | M | J | J | A | S | O | N | D |

Hoverfly
Eristalis pertinax

One of our most abundant hoverflies, and a very similar species to *E. tenax*; however, the male has a much more tapered abdomen than the drone fly. For a definitive difference between the two, check the tarsi of the front legs: in *E. pertinax* they are pale, and in *E. tenax* they are dark. May be found almost anywhere in Cornwall and the Isles of Scilly. There are seven other closely related species.

Stonefly
Leuctra species

Christened the needle fly by anglers, because when at rest the dark brown wings are wrapped tightly around its body. A common insect of rivers and streams, the larvae are aquatic, crawling out on to stones for the weak flying adults to emerge. Mature adults tend to remain near the water. This is one of a number of very similar species. Not IOS.

| J | F | M | A | M | J | J | A | S | O | N | D |

| J | F | M | A | M | J | J | A | S | O | N | D |

Alderfly

Sialis species

Usually seen near slow-moving or still water, at rest on marginal plants such as soft rush where the eggs are laid. Each cigar-shaped egg is placed individually, in clusters of 200 or more. Once hatched, the larvae fall into the water to begin an aquatic stage of up to two years. The relatively large, smoky-brown wings have thickened veins. BL=25mm. 6

Common Scorpion-fly

Panorpa communis

Takes its name from the tip of the male's abdomen (female shown here), which curls back over the body, looking very much like a scorpion's sting. This is for mating, and the insect is completely harmless. Viewed from the side, the scorpion-fly has a long, distinctive beak and sometimes feeds on dead insects in spiders' webs. Widespread in sunny, scrubby locations. One of three similar species.

J	F	M	A	M	J	J	A	S	O	N	D

J	F	M	A	M	J	J	A	S	O	N	D

Bees, Wasps, Ants and Relatives

With well over 6,000 species in the UK alone, bees, wasps, ants and their relatives belong to the largest order of insects in Britain, the Hymenoptera.

The members of this order vary considerably in size, but most have membranous wings with relatively few veins. In most hymenoptera there are two pairs of wings, the forewings and much smaller hindwings being linked on each side by a row of hooks to form a single unit.

Females of the order have ovipositors at the tip of the abdomen that are modified to serve as drills (as in ichneumons), saws (as in saw-flies), or stings (as in bees and wasps). Males do not possess a sting.

Among this order are many species of parasitic wasps and ichneumons that lay their eggs in the larvae of other insects, with the host remaining alive before being slowly consumed from within once the eggs have hatched. This may happen while the victim is still a caterpillar/larva, or once the host has pupated.

There are also a number of 'cuckoo' bees and wasps that lay their eggs in the nests of other species. Once hatched, the 'cuckoo' consumes both the egg or larvae and any food cell laid in by the host. Both social and solitary bees and wasps can be victims of this type of behaviour.

Bumblebees can be a deceptively difficult group of insects to identify as there may be considerable variation in both size and colour patterns in many of the 25 or so British species. They are important pollinators of fruit trees, flowers and some arable crops, but sadly these social insects have seriously declined in numbers.

Some species of Hymenoptera are accomplished builders and architects: for example, the social wasps that create large, multi-celled paper nests, sometimes as big as a football, from thousands of slivers of chewed wood. Other solitary species burrow into the ground to create nest chambers, some of which are even topped off with chimney- or funnel-like structures made of numerous tiny daubs of mud such as those belonging to the solitary wasp *Odynerus spinipes*. Potter wasps collect sand and mud to make individual, vase-shaped nests that are often

*The funnel-shaped entrance to the nest of the solitary wasp (*Odynerus spinipes*)*

attached to heather or fixed together in a small community.

Solitary bees and wasps may use the same area of ground for their nest burrows, but occupying the site at different stages of the season, thus avoiding direct competition between species.

Ants are notable among Hymenoptera in that they are largely wingless workers, with only the relatively small number of reproductive queens and males having wings. The most productive sites for sun-loving ants are south- or south-west-facing slopes with short, cropped vegetation. Some species of ants play very important roles in the life-cycle of other Cornish insects, including the extremely rare large blue butterfly (*Maculinea arion*). The large blue's larvae are taken into the nests of the red ant (*Myrmica sabuleti*), which are attracted to the sweet secretions of the caterpillars. Once in the nest, the large blue caterpillar feeds on young ant larvae until it is time for the adult butterfly to emerge.

Although only 20 or so species of ant have been recorded from Cornwall and the Isles of Scilly in recent years, it is difficult to identify individual species without specialist keys (see Further Reading, page 102), which require the use of a hand lens at the very least. They are therefore beyond the scope of this book.

In the species account for the ruby-tailed wasp, I have used the term 'agg' at the end of the Latin name – for example, *Chrysis ignita* agg. This is because there are seven similar species that are difficult to separate currently being reviewed by the scientific community, and as an interim measure the seven have been aggregated (agg) under one name.

*Red ants (*Myrmica *species) on the head of a flower, facing page*

Ruby-tailed Wasp
Chrysis ignita agg

This is the commonest example of seven species that are difficult to separate (aggregated together here). The adult seeks out the nests of solitary bees and wasps in which to lays its eggs, the resulting grubs eventually eating the larvae of their hosts. Active only in bright sunshine, if threatened by their host species the concave abdomen allows the adults to curl up into a ball so that only the hardest body parts are exposed. Widespread. Not IOS.

Ichneumon
Lissonota species

Ichneumons are a large group of parasitic insects. This female *Lissonota* demonstrates a striking feature of the group – the incredibly long ovipositor. When not in use, the ovipositor is housed in a long sheath that dwarfs the rest of the insect's body. As shown here, the ovipositor is capable of injecting deep into wood as the ichneumon probes the tree for the larvae of a moth in which to lay its egg.

J	F	M	A	M	J	J	A	S	O	N	D

Sand-tailed Digger Wasp
Cerceris arenaria

A solitary wasp that digs its nest burrows gregariously in areas of bare ground, which the female will stock with paralysed weevils. One of several similar species differentiated by facial patterns and the position of abdominal hair tufts. Each abdominal segment is separated by distinct grooves, giving it a bulbous look. Widespread, particularly around dune systems, but also inland at old mining sites. Not IOS.

Grey Mining Bee
Andrena cineraria

A white-faced mining bee that takes advantage of the legacy of Cornwall's industrial past by excavating its nesting burrows in bare patches of ground, often at ex-mining sites. These are solitary bees, but the nest burrows may be loosely congregated within an open area of soil. Males have a band of white hair around the otherwise black abdomen that is absent in the female. Widespread. Not IOS.

Honey Bee

Apis mellifera

Honey bees live in permanent communities of perhaps 50,000 insects, either within a man-made hive or in hollow trees in the wild. Inside the nest the wax combs are suspended vertically, each one consisting of a series of six-sided cells where larvae are reared and honey and pollen is stored. The colony is sustained over winter with food gathered during the summer. Widespread.

Early Bumblebee

Bombus pratorum

Often found in gardens, as well as on farmland and woodland edges, this widespread species is always one of the first bumblebees of spring. One of a number of similarly coloured species, though smaller than most, the males have yellow hairs on their faces. Nests underground in small colonies at the base of bushes, or in holes in trees.

| J | F | M | A | M | J | J | A | S | O | N | D |

| J | F | M | A | M | J | J | A | S | O | N | D |

Red-tailed Bumblebee
Bombus lapidarius

A very common and widespread species that frequently has subterranean nests, the queens and workers are generally all black with an orange tail, while males have yellow faces, yellowy/white bands on the black thorax, and an orange tip to the otherwise black abdomen. Note there are other similarly coloured species. Often abundant on coastal dunes, farmland and heathland, and in gardens and woodland clearings.

Common Carder-bee
Bombus pascuorum

This medium-sized bee takes its name from the species habit of collecting moss to build nest covers (a carder being an instrument with which to tease or comb out fibres). All casts are predominantly a pale ginger colour, with noticeable black patches on the abdomen (more so than other ginger species). Another very common and widespread species that has nests on or just below the ground; often abundant around coastal dunes, farmland, gardens, woodland clearings and heathland.

| J | F | M | A | M | J | J | A | S | O | N | D |

| J | F | M | A | M | J | J | A | S | O | N | D |

Beetles

On a walk through the countryside, we may notice the odd bumblebee, a few butterflies, and the odd annoying fly, but we seldom notice a beetle. So it may seem surprising that there are almost 4,000 species of beetles in the UK alone, filling every conceivable niche, though we are usually aware of only a tiny fraction of these.

Beetles belong to the order Coleoptera. They have an armoured appearance, with the front pairs of wings having become modified to form hard wing cases, or 'elytra'. The rear wings are folded beneath these two elytra, and so are protected. Beetles that can fly have two elytra meeting along a central divide down the abdomen. In some species that cannot fly, the two elytra are fused to form one toughened shell. In both instances, the elytra also provide protection to the abdomen and part of the thorax. However, there are species such as the rove beetles whose elytra are greatly reduced, leaving much of the abdomen exposed.

The female glow-worm is an example of a beetle with no wing cases/elytra or flight wings, and it looks very much like the larva of the species. The male does have fully developed elytra and wings, flying at night in search of the green light produced by the flightless female, the underside of the end of her abdomen glowing as she sits in low grass.

Beetles very often have legs adapted to the insect's own particular lifestyle. Some species that dig burrows, such as the dor beetles, have broadened legs which are strongly toothed and are ideal for digging. A number of aquatic beetles have hind legs thickened into paddle shapes, which are ideal for swimming.

Many, but not all, species of beetle have the ability to fly, although they can be somewhat clumsy in the air, and relatively little time is spent in flight.

Beetles and their larvae both have formidable biting jaws that allow them to exploit almost any potential food source, from the flesh of other animals and insects to living or dead plant material, including the timber from trees.

Like other insects, beetles have four distinct stages in their life history: the egg, larva, pupa and adult.

*A sexton beetle (*Nicrophorus investigator*) infested with mites*

Beetle larvae are extremely diverse, both in appearance and habits. In some species, such as cockchafers, the larvae live underground in the soil and look like large maggots. In others, such as the great diving beetle, the larvae are aquatic, and although very different in appearance from the adult, look superficially like fully formed insects in their own right. A number of terrestrial beetle larvae, such as the green tiger beetle, dig burrows into bare soil, where they lie in wait with their flattened heads flush across the mouth of the tunnel, ready to ambush their prey.

Ex-mining sites throughout the county are particularly important habitats for burrowing insects, as they often have open banks of silty tailings where mineral contaminants have retarded plant growth.

Most beetles pupate in the ground, under bark or in plant tissue, but some species, such as ladybirds, choose to hang freely from a plant or similar support.

The adult beetle emerging from the pupa is fully formed, and will not grow any further over its remaining lifetime.

In common with other insects, including bumblebees, beetles such as the sexton beetle (*Nicrophorus investigator*) on page 83 can be badly affected by mite infestations. In this instance, the mites are merely hitching a lift to their next meal, feeding on the maggots that frequent the carrion to which the beetle is attracted.

Some species of beetle are serious agricultural pests, one infamous example being the Colorado beetle, which can devastate a potato crop as both larvae and adults. To counter this, it is well known that ladybirds such as the seven-spot ladybird can be effective controllers of greenfly. Other species, such as the ground and rove beetles, are voracious predators, feeding on other insects, slugs and snails, while diving beetles will tackle tadpoles and even young fish. A number of species that feed on other invertebrates inject their prey with digestive juices before sucking out the liquefied contents.

Dung beetles consume significant amounts of dung, and so are important caretakers of the countryside. Sexton beetles perform much the same function with carrion.

Green Tiger Beetle
Cicindela campestris
A fierce predator as both an adult and a larva, with bulging eyes and massive cream-coloured jaws. Generally green with cream spots on the elytra; the legs and antennae have a pinky-purple tinge. BL=12–15mm. Common across heathlands and old mining sites, along areas of bare ground. Larvae live in burrows where they lie in wait for prey with their jaws flush to the entrance.

J	F	M	A	M	J	J	A	S	O	N	D

Rove Beetle

Staphylinus caesareus

A family of beetles distinguished by their short elytra, which resemble little waistcoats. When threatened, rove beetles may raise their tails in a menacing display, as if to sting; however, they are harmless. This impressive insect can be separated from similar species by the golden hairs running around the edge of the thorax. BL = 14–22mm. Found around dung or carrion, where it will prey on other insects.

Dor Beetle

Geotrupes species

A fairly large beetle, up to 25mm long, black in colour with a purple-blue sheen and ridged elytra. Feeds on dung. Commonly found walking along open footpaths, where it appears ungainly and sadly is often trodden on. One of nature's caretakers, the adults bury dung in a chamber for their larvae to feed on. The adults are often infested with mites.

| J | F | M | A | M | J | J | A | S | O | N | D |

| J | F | M | A | M | J | J | A | S | O | N | D |

Cockchafer

Melolontha melolontha

A large beetle (BL = 20–30mm) with a ridged, rosy, salmon-coloured elytra. Especially common throughout the month of May, giving rise to its other popular English name, the Maybug. The larvae live in the ground, and take three years to develop. Adults have a rather clumsy flight, and frequently clatter into obstacles. They usually fly in the evenings and are a favourite food of bats.

Rose Chafer

Cetonia aurata

A beautiful green, shiny beetle that may have varying degrees of a copper sheen and equally variable white streaks on the elytra. BL = 14–20mm. Feeds on a wide range of flowers, including roses, heathers and ivy, flying readily if disturbed. The larvae live in rotting timber and humus. A black subspecies, *pallida*, occurs widely on the Isles of Scilly alongside the normal form.

| J | F | M | A | M | J | J | A | S | O | N | D |

| J | F | M | A | M | J | J | A | S | O | N | D |

Thick-legged Flower Beetle
Oedemera nobilis
A striking iridescent green beetle (BL=8–10mm), commonly found on flower heads, where it feeds on pollen. Only the male has the swollen hind femora, which gives the beetle its English name. The species is also notable in that the two halves of the elytra are always spread slightly apart in both sexes. Widespread and common.

Oil Beetle
Meloe proscarabaeus
A large black beetle (BL=13–32mm) with a blue sheen that can exude a smelly, oily fluid as a defence mechanism. The antennae of the male are kinked, as in this example, while the abdomen of the larger female is very swollen, giving it an ungainly appearance. The larvae, sometimes known as bee lice, complete their development in solitary bee nests, where they feed on the host's egg. 18

J	F	M	A	M	J	J	A	S	O	N	D

J	F	M	A	M	J	J	A	S	O	N	D

Four-banded Longhorn Beetle

Leptura quadrifasciata

Longhorn beetles are characterized by their long and distinctive antennae. *L. quadrifasciata* has four clearly defined, wavy yellow bands across each of the black elytra. Widespread in broadleaved woodland where the larvae feed on dead wood. BL=10–20mm, excluding antennae. The very similar, nationally scarce golden-haired longhorn (*L. aurulenta*) has a golden fringe of hairs along the front and rear margins of the pronotum, and can be seen at 9.

Leaf Beetle

Chrysolina banksi

A very distinctive beetle, having a beautiful bronze sheen to its dimpled upper body, which gives it a beaten metal look that is in contrast to its bright red legs and antennae. Belongs to the large family of leaf-eating beetles, and has a ladybird-like outline. Slow-moving, and often found on low vegetation. BL=7–11mm.

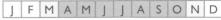

Bloody-nosed Beetle
Timarcha tenebricosa
A flightless beetle, which when alarmed ejects a drop of red liquid from its mouth. BL=11–18mm. This generally black insect has a bluish sheen to its rounded body. Common throughout Cornwall, it can often be found crawling slowly along bare ground or low vegetation, particularly in the spring.

Weevil
Liparus coronatus
Weevils are a distinctive group of beetles with prominent snouts, or rostrums, which also bear the antennae. *L. cornatus* has a scattering of distinctive golden scales on the side of the thorax (sometimes on the elytra), and a golden fringe along the rear edge of the thorax. The larvae feed on plant roots and may be a pest on carrots. Widespread but infrequent. BL=9–12mm.

J	F	M	A	M	J	J	A	S	O	N	D

J	F	M	A	M	J	J	A	S	O	N	D

Ladybirds

Ladybirds are a group of beetles often identifiable by the number of spots on the elytra.

24-spot Ladybird

Subcoccinella 24-punctata
Orangey-red; black/dark brown spots may be fused. Elytra covered in short, fine hairs. BL=3.5–4.5mm. Widespread in low-growing vegetation. *Bottom right D*

16-spot Ladybird

Tytthaspis 16-punctata
Dull mustard colour; black spots sometimes fused. Widespread in meadows, feeds on mildew. BL=2.5–3.5mm. *Bottom right A*

7-spot Ladybird

Coccinella 7-punctata
Very common, widespread. Adults and larvae beneficial in controlling aphids. BL=6.5–8mm. *Adult bottom left, larva middle right*

11-spot Ladybird

Coccinella 11-punctata
Widespread, particularly in coastal dunes. Eleventh spot common to both elytra. BL=3.5–5mm. *Bottom right C*

Orange Ladybird

Halyzia 16-guttata
Widespread, frequently found around sycamores. Orange with cream spots, transparent margin around elytra and thorax, covering head and eyes. BL=5–6.5mm. *Top middle*

22-spot Ladybird

Thea 22-punctata
Like many ladybirds the number of spots varies, in this case usually from 20 to 22. Widespread in meadows. BL=3–4.5mm. *Top left*

Cream-spot Ladybird

Calvia 14-guttata
Widespread along hedgerows and deciduous woodland margins. Orangey-brown, 14 cream spots across elytra. BL=4–5mm. *Bottom right B*

Harlequin Ladybird

Harmonia axyridis
Rapidly spreading, arrived in Britain from northern Europe in summer 2004. Patterns variable, from black with two red spots to red with 21 black spots. BL=7–8mm. Considered a threat to native ladybirds. *Top right*

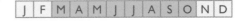

Aquatic Insects

Many terrestrial insects have larval stages that are aquatic. However, all the insects in this section are aquatic as adults, either in the water or on the surface of the water.

Perhaps the most diverse and highly visible groups of aquatic insects are the water bugs belonging to the order Hemiptera, with over 60 species known and recorded in Britain.

The surface-dwellers are all highly predatory, and quickly descend on any dead or dying insects that fall on to the water. The surface of the water is in a state of tension, like an elastic skin, allowing species like the common pond skater (*Gerris lacustris*) to sit on the surface and pick up small vibrations from likely prey items.

Below the water surface there are many beetles. Some feed on vegetation, others, like the great diving beetle, are highly carnivorous. Each insect must return to the surface for air, many having fine hairs on the underside of the body in order to trap as much air as possible to prolong their stay underwater. Some water bugs, such as the large water stick insect (*Ranatra linearis*) have developed long breathing tubes, which act as a snorkel.

Great Diving Beetle
Dytiscus marginalis

A large green aquatic beetle (BL = 26–35mm), with golden-yellow margins around the abdomen and pronotum. The underside is golden-yellow. The male's elytra is smooth, the female's ridged. Both larvae and adults are voracious predators, tackling prey like small fish or frogs. Common and widespread pond-dwellers. Not IOS. This male is probably infected with parasites. 6, 11, 12, 18

| J | F | M | A | M | J | J | A | S | O | N | D |

River Skater
Aquarius najas

A large, surface-dwelling insect (BL=13–17mm), commonly found on slow-flowing stretches of river. Usually wingless, the first segment of the antennae is longer than the second and third put together. In the similar, but usually winged *A. paludum*, the first segment is shorter than the second and third put together. Not IOS. There are several other very similar *Gerris* species pond skaters.

Water Scorpion
Nepa cinerea

A striking scorpion lookalike, the long tail on this harmless aquatic insect is actually a breathing tube rather than a sting. Moves slowly through the weedy margins of muddy pools, hiding in wait for invertebrate prey, before grasping them with its front legs and sucking out all their juices through its beak. Fully winged, but seldom flies. Not IOS. 6, 11, 12, 17, 18

| J | F | M | A | M | J | J | A | S | O | N | D |

| J | F | M | A | M | J | J | A | S | O | N | D |

Saucer Bug

Ilyocoris cimicoides

A fully winged insect that cannot fly, so it must walk between the weedy ponds where it lives. Oval in outline, but relatively flat, the saucer bug swims with air trapped under the forewings and the underside of its body, searching for other aquatic invertebrates to prey on. During the winter, it may hibernate at the bottom of the pond in cold conditions. Probably widespread but under-recorded. Not IOS. 12

Water Boatman

Notonecta obliqua

Sometimes known as a back-swimmer, this restless water bug swims on its boat-shaped back. It detects prey as large as tadpoles and small fish, by sight and vibration. The water boatman will readily take to the air in warm weather, and if caught can inflict a piercing bite with its beak. One of four similar species that can be provisionally separated by the forewing pattern of mature adults. 6, 7, 12

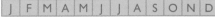

Site Gazetteer

1 **Porthgwarra:** Access point and car-parking (fee) at SW371217. Explore heathland between Gwennap Head and Carn Glaze for butterflies, grasshoppers and crickets.

2 **Upton Towans, Hayle, CWT reserve:** Access point and limited car-parking at SW579396. Good for butterflies, moths, grasshoppers and crickets.

3 **St Gothian Sands, Gwithian, CC LNR:** Access point and roadside car-parking at SW586416, additional parking at SW586413. Main dragonfly interest at SW582416 (gated access to fenced wetland – dog deterrent only). Butterfly interest centred at SW584415. Also good for moths, grasshoppers and crickets.

4 **Great Wheal Seton, Red River Valley, Camborne, CC LNR:** Access point and limited roadside parking at SW658418, Tolvaddon. Main dragonfly interest at SW655418. A classic ex-tin-streaming site.

5 **Kynance Cove, Lizard peninsula, NT NNR:** Access point and car-parking (fee for non-NT members) at SW688131. Explore surrounding heathlands, main butterfly interest towards Holestrow Quarry at SW691129. Also good for grasshoppers and crickets.

6 **Windmill Farm and Ruan Pool, Lizard peninsula, CWT/CBWPS reserve:** Access point, car-parking and information centre at SW694152. Main dragonfly

interest at SW689155. Good for butterflies, dragonflies, grasshoppers and crickets.

7 **Croft Pascoe Pool and Plantation, Goonhilly Downs, NE NNR:** Access points and limited roadside parking at SW731197 (pool) and SW729193 (plantation). Dragonflies from the pool can be found maturing, sheltering or roosting along the glades of the plantation. Also good for grasshoppers and crickets.

8 **Gear Sands/Penhale Sands, Perranporth, CC managed/MOD property:** Access point and roadside car-parking at SW774553. Main butterfly interest centred at SW770563 near St Piran's Oratory. Access to MOD area requires permission. Also good for moths, grasshoppers and crickets.

9 **Chyverton, Zelah, CWT reserve:** Access point and limited roadside parking at SW789513. Follow the track into the reserve heading north-east. Dragonfly interest centred on the wet heathland and pool, butterfly interest centred on the woodland edges and meadows.

10 **Rock Dunes:** Access point and car-parking (fee) at SW928758. Explore dunes towards Brea Hill. Good for butterflies, grasshoppers and crickets.

11 **Goss Moor, NE, NNR:** Explore the moor via the network of cycle routes and footpaths. Butterfly interest centred at SW935597 (St Dennis Junction), dragonfly interest centred at SW963601 (Tregoss). The whole of the moor with its extensive wetlands is of interest.

12 **Breney Common, CWT reserve:** Car-parking at Lowertown/Gunwen Chapel, SX0562612. Walk 200 metres south along the minor road before crossing the river and following a dirt track to your left. Access to the reserve at SX054609. Main dragonfly interest at SX056610, main butterfly interest at SX054608.

13 **Bunny's Hill, Cardinham:** Access point and car-parking at SX117674 (along track leading west from triangular road junction). Explore area north of track for butterflies.

14 **Bowithick, Davidstow:** Access point and car-parking at SX183826. Follow track heading south-west with dragonfly interest throughout the extensive boggy pools and marshes.

15 **Polson Bridge, River Tamar, Launceston:** Access point and car-parking in lay-by at SX353848. Dragonfly interest centred along the river bank from just east of the lay-by, through the fishing area, to the road bridge.

16 **Greenscoombe Wood, Luckett, CWT reserve:** Car-parking in the village car-park at SX389736. From there, follow the minor road running to the south-east on foot. The access point to the wood and information board is at SX391731. Main butterfly interest at SX391725.

17 **Rame Head and Penlee Point, part CWT reserve:** Access point and car-parking at SX421487 (Rame Head), or SX436491 (Penlee CWT reserve). A good area for migrant insects, the coastal footpath runs between the two sites.

18 **Marsland, CWT/DWT reserve:** Access point and severely limited roadside parking at SS217169. Walk down into the valley, heading towards Gooseham Mill. Permit required for full access (contact DWT). Good for butterflies and dragonflies.

Glossary

- **abdomen** – The third part of an insect's body, at the opposite end from the head.

- **elytra** – Shell-like casing formed from the hardened forewings of an insect.

- **exuvia/exuviae** (plural) – The cast skin of a dragonfly larva after the flying adult has emerged.

- **femur/femora** (plural) – Long leg section between an insect's 'knee' and thorax.

- **herbivore** – Vegetarian, plant-eater.

- **instar** – Stage in a nymph's development between moults before becoming fully adult.

- **longitudinal** – Running lengthwise.

- **ocelli** – Simple eyes, consisting of a number of light-sensitive cells and a single lens

- **omnivorous** – Feeding on both animal and plant tissue.

- **oviposit/ovipositing** – Egg-laying.

- **ovipositor** – Female egg-laying organ.

- **proboscis** – Tubular protrusion on the head of an insect used for sucking up liquids or nectar.

- **pronotum** – Upper surface of the first segment of the thorax.

- **prothorax** – First segment (nearest the head) of the thorax.

- **pruinescence** – A waxy bloom of colour that develops on mature insects, but may be at least partly rubbed off by contact with another surface.

- **tarsus/tarsi** (plural) – Segmented foot or feet.

- **tergite** – The top surface of an abdominal segment.

Index of Insects

Note: Insects are grouped in species, in the same order as in the book. Within the species, they are listed alphabetically by common name, followed by scientific name and page number.

Further Reading

Brooks, S., 1997 (2002), *Field Guide to the Dragonflies and Damselflies of Great Britain and Ireland*. British Wildlife Publishing, Hook.

Chinery, Michael, 1986, *Collins Guide to the Insects of Britain and Western Europe*. Collins, London.

Edwards, M. and Jenner, M., 2005 (2009), *Field Guide to the Bumblebees of Great Britain and Ireland*. Ocelli.

Marshall, Judith A. and Haes, E.C.M., 1988, *Grasshoppers and Allied Insects of Great Britain and Ireland*. Harley Books, Colchester.

Skinner, Gary J. and Allen, Geoffrey W.,1996, *Ants*. Richmond Publishing, Naturalists' Handbook no. 24, Slough.

Stubbs, Alan E. and Falk, Steven J., 2002, *British Hoverflies*. The British Entomological and Natural History Society, London.

Waring, P. and Townsend, M., 2003, *Field Guide to the Moths of Great Britain and Ireland*. British Wildlife Publishing, Hook.

Organizations and Websites

Many of the organizations listed below arrange local field meetings throughout the year. These friendly events can be a very useful way of exploring our most prolific wildlife sites and discovering the exact location for many of our most fascinating insects. They also provide a great opportunity for beginners to learn from experienced enthusiasts.

Bees, Wasps and Ants Recording Scheme

The national society dedicated to studying and recording bees, wasps and ants in Britain and Ireland. Website: www.bwars.com

British Bugs

An online identification guide to the UK's bugs. Website: www.britishbugs.org.uk

British Dragonfly Society

Promotes the conservation of dragonflies and damselflies, and organizes the national recording scheme as well as field meetings across the country. Website: www.dragonflysoc.org.uk

Bumblebee Conservation Trust

UK organization promoting bumblebee conservation and research. Website: www.bumblebeeconservation.org.uk

Butterfly Conservation

Organization dedicated to saving wild butterflies, moths and their habitats. Organizes field meetings throughout the country via its network of local branches. Cornwall branch. National website: www.butterfly-conservation.org. Cornwall Branch website: www.cornwall-butterfly-conservation.org.uk

Cornish Nature

The author's website includes information about Cornish dragonflies and damselflies: www.cornishnature.co.uk

Cornwall Wildlife Trust

Leading conservation body devoted to the county's wildlife, manages 55 reserves across the county. A full and varied programme of field trips organized each year. Website: www.cornwallwildlifetrust.org.uk

ERCCIS

The Environmental Records Centre for Cornwall and the Isles of Scilly collects and manages all wildlife records for the county. Also organizes local wildlife field study courses. Website: www.erccis.co.uk

Hoverfly Recording Scheme

National recording scheme incorporating the Dipterists Forum, offering help with the identification of flies. Website: www.hoverfly.org.uk

Orthoptera Recording Scheme

National recording scheme for grasshoppers and crickets, earwigs, cockroaches, stick insects and mantids. Includes audio files of grasshopper and cricket songs. Website: www.orthoptera.org.uk

A female broad-bodied chaser (Libellula depressa). See page 23.